How to wash a WOOLLY mammoth

MICHELLE ROBINSON · KATE HINDLEY

SIMON AND SCHUSTER
London New York Sydney Toronto New Delhi

Does your woolly mammoth need a wash?
It's not a very easy thing to do . . .

Woolly mammoths are quite BIG
and wool is notoriously tricky to clean.
Don't worry, just follow this step-by-step guide.

STEP ONE:
Fill the bath tub.

Fig. 1: Empty

Fig. 2: Full

If your mammoth is feeling thirsty, this may take a while.

STEP TWO:

Add bubbles.

STEP THREE:
Add mammoth.

Fig. 1: Broom

Fig. 2: Spooky mask

Fig. 3: Skateboard

Fig. 4: Heavy-duty crane

When all else fails,
there is always cake.

STEP FOUR:
Start scrubbing!
Don't forget to wash
behind those ears . . .

STEP FIVE:
Wash his big, fat tummy.

CAREFUL -
a mammoth's tummy is terribly tickly!

STEP SIX:
Make a SPLASH!

STEP SEVEN:
Now for the really WOOLLY bit.

You're going to need some shampoo - not too much!

Fig. 1:
...ble bliss

Fig. 2:
Who me?

Fig. 3:
Hair-raising

Fig. 4:
...mmoth
...llet

Fig. 5:
And that is?

Fig. 6:
Twirly-
whirly

Fig. 7:
...e King

Fig. 8:
Comb-over

Be CAREFUL
not to get any in
the mammoth's . . .

That's torn it!

STEP EIGHT:
To get a wet woolly mammoth down
from a tree, you'll need . . . .

...a very STRONG trampoline.

STEP NINE:

Let him share a bath with YOU!

STEP TEN: Throw in the towel and SNUGGLE.